Violin Grade 2

Pieces

for Trinity College London examinations

2010-2015

Published by
Trinity College London

Registered Office:
4th floor, 89 Albert Embankment
London SE1 7TP UK

T +44 (0)20 7820 6100
F +44 (0)20 7820 6161
E music@trinitycollege.co.uk
www.trinitycollege.co.uk

Registered in the UK
Company no. 02683033
Charity no. 1014792

Music processed by New Notations London and Moira Roach.
Printed in England by Halstan, Amersham, Bucks.

Bourée

from a *Wedding Divertissement*

Georg Philipp Telemann
(1681–1767)

Dynamics are editorial.

Square Dance

from *Little Suite no. 4*

Peter Martin

The Flop-Eared Mule

Traditional American

This piece may be played unaccompanied in the examination.

Move It!

Richard Kershaw

(*1*) The bottom notes of the violin part may be omitted in the examination (bars 21-28).

Circus March

Robert Trory and Sally Mays

La cucaracha

Traditional Spanish

Hurdy Gurdy

from *Album for the Young* op. 39 no. 24

Pytor Ilyich Tchaikovsky
(1840-1893)

Violin Grade 2

Pieces

for Trinity College London examinations

2010-2015

Published by
Trinity College London

Registered Office:
4th floor, 89 Albert Embankment
London SE1 7TP UK

T +44 (0)20 7820 6100
F +44 (0)20 7820 6161
E music@trinitycollege.co.uk
www.trinitycollege.co.uk

Registered in the UK
Company no. 02683033
Charity no. 1014792

Music processed by New Notations London and Moira Roach.
Printed in England by Halstan, Amersham, Bucks.

TG 008244
ISBN 978-0-85736-060-1

Bourée

from a *Wedding Divertissement*

Georg Philipp Telemann
(1681-1767)

Dynamics are editorial.

Square Dance

from *Little Suite no. 4*

Peter Martin

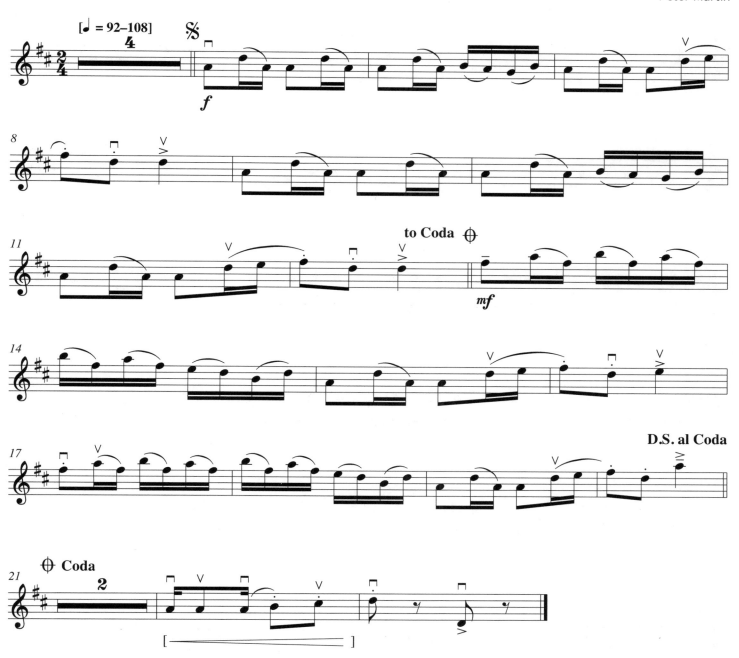

The Flop-Eared Mule

Traditional American

This piece may be played unaccompanied in the examination.

Move It!

Richard Kershaw

(*1*) The bottom notes of the violin part may be omitted in the examination (bars 21-28).

Circus March

Robert Trory and Sally Mays

La cucaracha

Traditional Spanish

Hurdy Gurdy

from *Album for the Young* op. 39 no. 24

Pytor Ilyich Tchaikovsky
(1840-1893)

Première Valse

Adam Carse
(1878-1958)

The Railroad Corral

Polly Waterfield and Louise Beach

Lonely Tune

from *Simple Suite no. 2*, op. 54 no. 4

Bernard Barrell
(1919-2005)

Première Valse

Adam Carse
(1878-1958)

D.C. al Fine

The Railroad Corral

Polly Waterfield and Louise Beach

Lonely Tune

from *Simple Suite no. 2*, op. 54 no. 4

Bernard Barrell
(1919-2005)

rit. poco al fine